SCHOLASTIC

MATHS
SATs TESTS
YEAR 2

SCHOLASTIC

Book End, Range Road, Witney, Oxfordshire, OX29 0YD
www.scholastic.co.uk
© 2018 Scholastic Ltd
1 2 3 4 5 6 7 8 9   8 9 0 1 2 3 4 5 6 7

A British Library Cataloguing-in-Publication Data
A catalogue record for this book is available from the
British Library.

ISBN 978-1407-18298-8

Printed and bound by Ashford Colour Press

Author

Ann Montague-Smith

Series consultant

Paul Hollin

Editorial team

Rachel Morgan, Jenny Wilcox, Mark Walker,
Mary Nathan, Kate Baxter, Janette Ratcliffe

Illustrations

Tom Heard and Moreno Chiacchiera

Design

Nicolle Thomas and Oxford Designers and Illustrators

Cover illustrations

Istock/calvindexter and Tomek.gr / Shutterstock/Visual Generation

Acknowledgements

Extracts from Department for Education website ©
Crown Copyright. Reproduced under the terms of the
Open Government Licence (OGL). www.nationalarchives.
gov.uk/doc/open-government-licence/version/3/

Every effort has been made to trace copyright holders
for the works reproduced in this publication, and the
publishers apologise or any inadvertent omissions.

Contents
Mathematics: Year 2

About this book

This book provides you with practice papers to help support children with the Key Stage 1 Mathematics test.

Using the practice papers

The practice papers in this book can be used as you would any other practice materials. The children need to be familiar with specific test-focused skills, such as ensuring equipment functions properly, leaving questions if they seem too difficult, working at a suitable pace for the tests and checking through their work.

If you choose to use the papers for revising content rather than practising tests, do be aware of the time factor. These tests are short at only 20 or 35 minutes per paper, as they are testing the degree of competence children have. The tests do not have to be completed within the times given since the ability to answer questions at pace is not part of Key Stage 1 assessment.

Equipment

The following equipment will be needed for all test papers.

- pencil/black pen
- eraser

About the tests

Each maths test has two papers:

- Paper 1: arithmetic – these are context-free calculations. The children have approximately 20 minutes to answer the questions. 25 marks are available. A practice question is provided at the start of the paper.

- Paper 2: reasoning – these are mathematical reasoning problems both in context and out of context. The children have approximately 35 minutes to answer the questions. 35 marks are available. A practice question is provided at the start of the paper and then followed by five aural questions.

The papers should be taken in order and children may have a break between papers. Neither paper should be strictly timed. You should ensure that every child has enough time to demonstrate what he or she understands, knows and can do, without prolonging the test inappropriately. Use your judgement to decide when, or if, children need breaks during the assessment, and whether to stop the text early if appropriate.

Do the practice question for each test together and ensure the children write their answer in the correct place.

All of the tests broadly increase in difficulty as they progress, and it is not expected that all children will be able to answer all of the questions. All questions can be read aloud so that reading ability does not affect a child's ability to demonstrate their mathematical skills.

The marks available for each question are shown in the test paper next to each question and are also shown next to each answer in the mark scheme.

Aural questions

There are five aural questions in paper 2. They are shown by this symbol. These questions should be read aloud following the script on page 94 of this book.

Advice for parents and carers

How this book will help

This book will support your child to get ready for the KS1 National Mathematics test. It provides valuable practice and help on the responses and content expected of Year 2 children aged 6–7 years.

In the weeks leading up to the National Tests, your child may be given plenty of practice, revision and tips to give them the best possible chance to demonstrate their knowledge and understanding. It is helpful to try to practise outside of school and many children benefit from extra input. This book will help your child to prepare and build their confidence.

In this book you will find two Mathematics tests. The layout and format of each test closely matches those used in the National Tests so your child will become familiar with what to expect and get used to the style of the tests. There is a comprehensive answer section and guidance about how to mark the questions.

Tips

- Make sure that you allow your child to take the test in a quiet environment where they are not likely to be interrupted or distracted.
- Make sure your child has a flat surface to work on, with plenty of space to spread out and good light.
- Emphasise the importance of reading and re-reading a question.
- These tests are similar to the ones your child will take in May in Year 2 and they therefore give you a good idea of strengths and areas for development. When you have found areas that require some more practice, it is useful to go over these again and practise similar types of question with your child.
- Go through the tests again together, identify any gaps in learning and address any misconceptions or areas of misunderstanding. If you are unsure of anything yourself, then make an appointment to see your child's teacher who will be able to help and advise further.
- Practising little and often will enable your child to build up confidence and skills over a period of time.

Advice for children

- Revise and practise regularly.
- Spend some time each week practising.
- Focus on the areas you are less sure of to get better.
- Get a good night's sleep and eat a healthy breakfast.
- Be on time for school.
- Make sure you have all the things you need.
- If a questions asks you to 'Show your method' then there will be marks if you get the method correct even if your answer is wrong.
- Leave out questions you do not understand and come back to them when you have completed those you can do.
- Check that you haven't missed any questions or pages out.

Test coverage

The test content is divided into strands and sub-strands. These are listed, for each question, in a table at the end of every test to allow tracking of difficulties. In a small number of cases, where practical equipment such as containers would be required, these aspects are not tested.

Strand	Sub-strand
Number and place value	counting (in multiples)
	read, write, order and compare numbers
	identify, represent and rounding
	number problems
Addition, subtraction, multiplication and division (calculations)	add/subtract mentally
	add/subtract using written methods
	use inverses and check
	add/subtract to solve problems
	multiply/divide mentally
	multiply/divide using written methods
	solve problems based on all four operations and knowledge of the commutative facts
	order operations
Fractions	recognise, find, write, name and count fractions
	equivalent fractions
Measurement	compare, describe and order measures
	measure and read scales
	money
	telling time, ordering time and units of time
	solve mathematical problems involving measures
Geometry – properties of shape	recognise and name common shapes
	describe properties and classify shapes
	draw and make shapes and relate 2D and 3D shapes
Geometry – position and direction	patterns
	describe position, direction and movement
Statistics	interpret and represent data
	solve problems involving data

Mathematics

Test A: Paper 1

Instructions Test A: Paper 1

- You have around **20 minutes** to complete this test paper.

- You may **not use** a calculator for any questions in this test paper.

- Work as quickly and carefully as you can.

- Try to answer all the questions. If you cannot do one of the questions, **go on to the next one**. You can come back to it later, if you have time.

- If you finish before the end, **go back and check your work**.

- Ask your teacher if you are not sure what to do.

Follow the instructions for each question carefully.

If you need to do working out, you can use any space on the page – do not use rough paper.

SCHOLASTIC National Curriculum SATs Tests

Practice question

6 + 3 = $\boxed{9}$

1.

$4 + 9 =$ | 13 |

Marks

1

2.

$17 - 10 =$ | 7 |

1

3.

8 + 6 + 6 = 20

14 + 6 = 20

Marks

1

4.

37 + 10 = 47

1

5. $25 - 6 =$ 19

Marks

1

6. $34 + 7 =$ 41

1

7. $20 - 19 =$ 1

1

8.

$7 + \boxed{4} = 11$

Marks

1

9.

$63 - 30 = \boxed{3\ 3}$

$$\begin{array}{r} 5\,\overset{}{\cancel{6}}\overset{}{\cancel{3}}{}^{1} \\ -\ 3\ 0 \\ \hline \end{array} \qquad \begin{array}{r} 6\ 3 \\ -\ 3\ 0 \\ \hline 3\ 3 \end{array}$$

1

10.

26 + 16 = 42

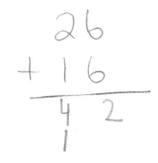

Marks

1

11.

0 × 2 = 2

1

12.

17 + 10 + 2 = 29

1

13.

70 –  2 0 = 50

1

14.

$10 \times 6 = \boxed{60}$

Marks

1

15.

$\frac{1}{2}$ of $40 = \boxed{20}$

1

Marks

16.

$15 \div 3 =$ | 5 |

1

17.

$38 + 54 =$ | 92 |

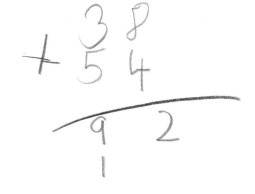

1

18.

$5 \times 5 = \boxed{25}$

1

19.

$\dfrac{3}{4}$ of 8 = $\boxed{6}$

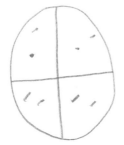

1

20.

$64 - 26 =$ 338

Marks

1

21.

$50 - 28 =$ 22

1

Marks

22. $\dfrac{1}{4}$ of 16 = $\boxed{4}$

1

23. 40 + 50 + 5 = $\boxed{95}$

1

SCHOLASTIC National Curriculum SATs Tests

24.

57 + | 28 | = 85

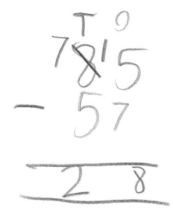

Marks

1

25.

$\frac{2}{3}$ of 15 = | 10 |

1

Test A: Paper 1 Marks

Q	Question	Possible marks	Actual marks
1	4 + 9	1	
2	17 − 10	1	
3	8 + 6 + 6	1	
4	37 + 10	1	
5	25 − 6	1	
6	34 + 7	1	
7	20 − 19	1	
8	7 + ☐ = 11	1	
9	63 − 30	1	
10	26 + 16	1	
11	0 × 2	1	
12	17 + 10 + 2	1	
13	70 − ☐ = 50	1	
14	10 × 6	1	
15	$\frac{1}{2}$ of 40	1	
16	15 ÷ 3	1	
17	38 + 54	1	
18	5 × 5	1	
19	$\frac{3}{4}$ of 8	1	
20	64 − 26	1	
21	50 − 28	1	
22	$\frac{1}{4}$ of 16	1	
23	40 + 50 + 5	1	
24	57 + ☐ = 85	1	
25	$\frac{2}{3}$ of 15	1	
	Total	**25**	

SCHOLASTIC National Curriculum SATs Tests

Mathematics

Test A: Paper 2

- You have around **35 minutes** to complete this test paper.
- You may **not use** a calculator for any questions in this test paper.
- Work as quickly and carefully as you can.
- Try to answer all the questions. If you cannot do one of the questions, **go on to the next one**. You can come back to it later, if you have time.
- If you finish before the end, **go back and check your work**.
- Ask your teacher if you are not sure what to do.

Follow the instructions for each question carefully.

If you need to do working out, you can use any space on the page – do not use rough paper.

Show your method

You may get extra marks if you show your method when you see this box.

> ✏️ Show your method.

Aural questions

Any questions which have this icon will be read aloud to you. (The script is on page 94.)

Marks

Practice question 👂

1. 👂

1

SCHOLASTIC National Curriculum SATs Tests

2.

Marks

triangle

square

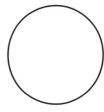

rectangle

circle

1

3.

Marks

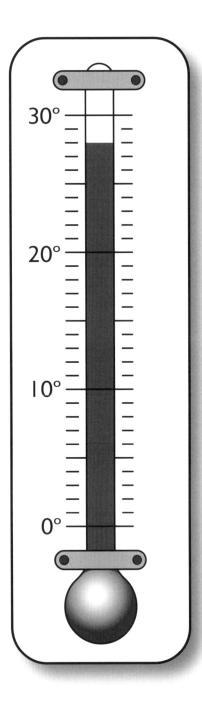

°C

1

Marks

4.

Apples	ЖӉ |||
Oranges	ЖӉ ЖӉ ||
Bananas	ЖӉ	

1

5. 👂

Marks

1

Marks

6. Look at these numbers.

45   **63**

Write the correct number in each box.

61 < ☐

54 > ☐

1

7. Mark this homework with a ✓ or ✗.

15 + 3 = 3 + 15   ☐

15 − 3 = 3 − 15   ☐

1

8. Circle the 10s digit in each of these numbers.

34   28   93

Circle the ones digit in each of these numbers.

24   73   66

Marks

1

---

9. Draw the next symbol in the pattern.

 ★ ■ ■ ○ ★ ■ ■ _____

1

SCHOLASTIC National Curriculum SATs Tests

10. Paul spends 13p.

How much change does he get from 20p?

	p

1

---

11. Write the correct sign in the box.
Choose from **+**, **−**, **×**, **÷**

18 [ ] 2 = 9

1

Marks

12. Ajay looks at the price of notebooks in four different shops.

Bargains   45p

Lucky   35p

Shoppy   52p

Macco   29p

Which shop sells the cheapest notebook?

1

SCHOLASTIC National Curriculum SATs Tests

Marks

13. Write the total of these coins.

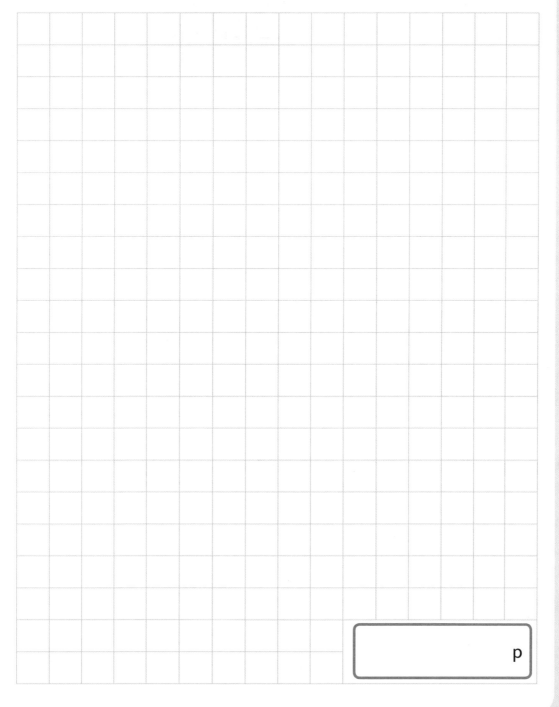

p

1

14.　　**a.** Estimate the number that goes in the box.
Write it in.

Marks

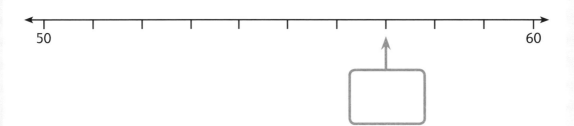

1

b. Now decide where 52 would go. Mark that
on the number line with an arrow to show
where it goes.

1

SCHOLASTIC National Curriculum SATs Tests

Marks

15. Oranges cost **15p** each and bananas cost **20p** each.

Fran buys **2 oranges** and **2 bananas**.

How much **change** does she get from **£1**?

Show your method.

p

2

16. These parcels have been weighed.

Marks

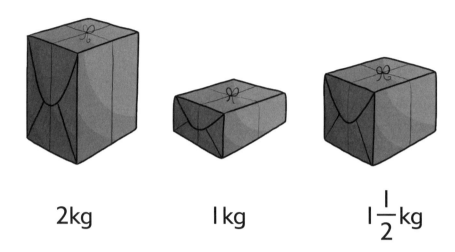

2kg   1 kg $1\frac{1}{2}$kg

a. Write these weights in order, starting with the lightest.

_____   _____   _____   1

b. Look at these signs.

Write the correct sign in each box.

2kg ☐ 1kg

1kg ☐ $1\frac{1}{2}$kg   1

SCHOLASTIC National Curriculum SATs Tests

Marks

17. There were some people on a train.

19 people get off the train at the first stop.

17 people get on the train.

Now there are 63 people on the train.

How many people were on the train to begin with?

 Show your method.

2

18. Write the missing numbers in this number pattern.

a. 0, 3, 6, _____, _____, _____, _____

1

b. Count back in 3s from 48 to 36. Write each number.

_____, _____, _____, _____, _____

1

Marks

19. Complete the chart for the shapes.

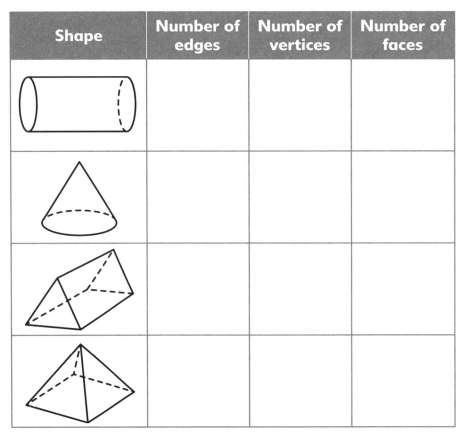

Shape	Number of edges	Number of vertices	Number of faces

2

20. 56 boys and 38 girls went on a school trip.
How many children was that altogether?

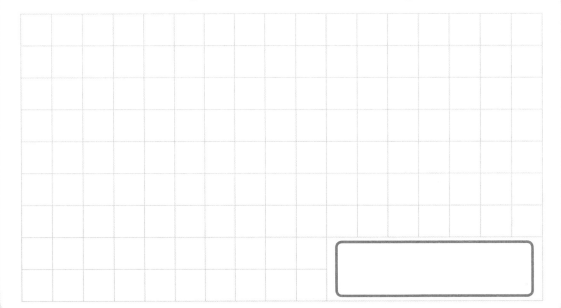

1

21. Draw lines to match the times to the clocks.

One has been done to help you.

10 o'clock

25 past 7

quarter to 3

twenty-five to 12

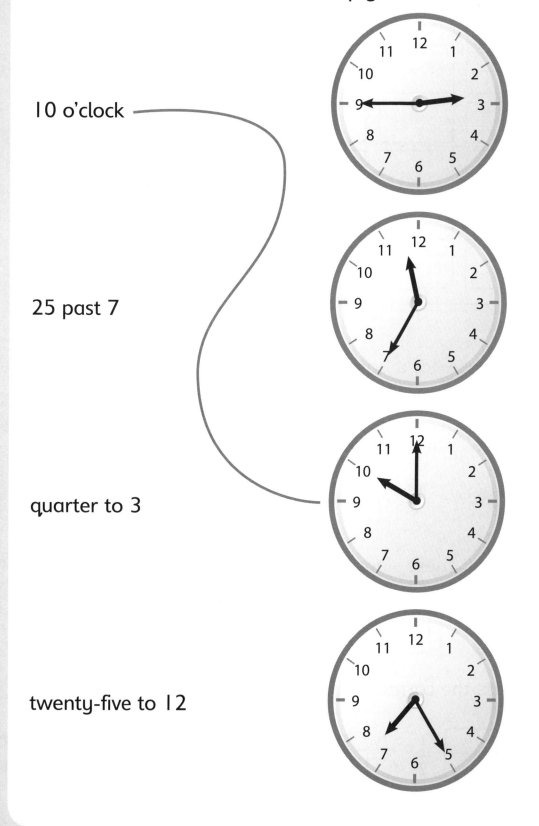

1

22. A bar of chocolate has 24 squares.

Marks

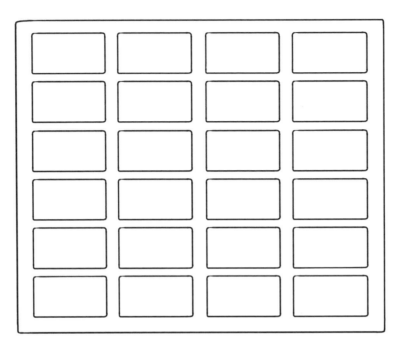

a. Mia has $\frac{2}{4}$ of a bar of chocolate.

Paul says he has $\frac{1}{2}$ of the bar of chocolate.

Shade $\frac{2}{4}$ of the chocolate.

1

b. Look at these signs.

      ☐ =

Write the correct sign in the box.

$\frac{2}{4}$ ☐ $\frac{1}{2}$

1

SCHOLASTIC National Curriculum SATs Tests

23. Elle shares equally 20 counters between a red pot and a green pot.

Ajay shares another 16 between the red pot and the green pot.

How many counters are there altogether in the red pot?

Marks

Show your method.

2

24. This block graph shows how many animals were in the animal sanctuary.

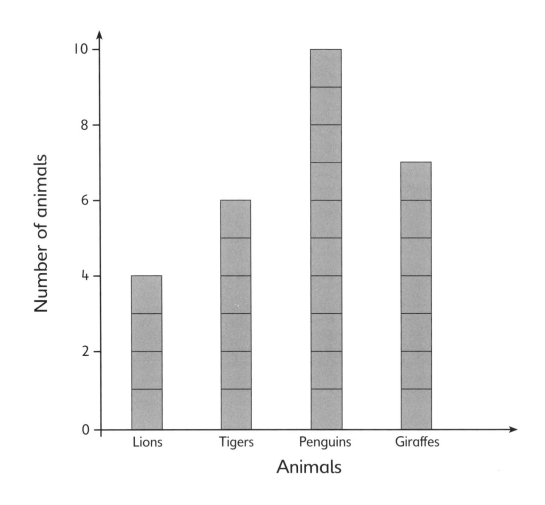

a. How many tigers are there?

1

b. How many fewer giraffes are there than penguins?

1

Marks

25. This is a plan of a village.

a. Follow the directions and draw the route from home to the school.

Start at home.
Turn right.
Follow the road to the crossroads.
Turn right.
Stop at the school.

1

b. Follow the directions and draw the route from the school to the shop.

Start at the school.
Turn right.
Follow the road to the crossroads.
Turn left.
Stop at the shop.

1

Test A: Paper 2 Marks

Q	Strand	Sub-strand	Possible marks	Actual marks
1	Addition and subtraction	Add/subtract mentally	1	
2	Geometry – properties of shapes	Recognise and name common shapes	1	
3	Measurement	Estimate, measure and read scales	1	
4	Statistics	Interpret and represent data	1	
5	Fractions	Recognise, find, name and write fractions	1	
6	Number and place value	Read, write, order and compare numbers	1	
7	Addition and subtraction	Order of numbers in addition and subtraction	1	
8	Number and place value	Place value	1	
9	Geometry – position and direction	Patterns	1	
10	Measurement	Solve problems involving money	1	
11	Multiplication and division	Use multiplication (×), division (÷) and equals (=) signs	1	
12	Number and place value	Read, write, order and compare numbers	1	
13	Measurement	Money	1	
14	Number and place value	Identify, represent and estimate; rounding	2	
15	Addition and subtraction	Solve problems with addition and subtraction	2	
16	Measurement	Compare and order measures	2	
17	Addition and subtraction	Estimate, use inverses and check	2	
18	Number and place value	Count in steps	2	
19	Geometry – properties of shapes	Describe properties and classify shapes	2	
20	Addition and subtraction	Solve problems with addition and subtraction	1	
21	Measurement	Telling time	1	
22	Fractions	Recognise, find, name and write fractions; equivalent fractions	2	
23	Multiplication and division	Solve problems involving multiplication and division	2	
24	Statistics	Solve problems involving data	2	
25	Geometry – position and direction	Describe position, direction and movement	2	
		Total	**35**	

SCHOLASTIC National Curriculum SATs Tests

Mathematics

Test B: Paper 1

Instructions Test B: Paper 1

- You have around **20 minutes** to complete this test paper.

- You may **not use** a calculator for any questions in this test paper.

- Work as quickly and carefully as you can.

- Try to answer all the questions. If you cannot do one of the questions, **go on to the next one**. You can come back to it later, if you have time.

- If you finish before the end, **go back and check your work**.

- Ask your teacher if you are not sure what to do.

Follow the instructions for each question carefully.

If you need to do working out, you can use any space on the page – do not use rough paper.

SCHOLASTIC National Curriculum SATs Tests

Practice question

Marks

5 − 3 = ☐

1.

$3 + 8 =$ [ ]

Marks

1

2.

$17 - 10 =$ [ ]

1

3.

$58 + 9 =$ [ ]

1

4.

$$4 + 8 + 3 = \boxed{}$$

1

5.

$$35 - 11 = \boxed{}$$

1

6.

$$10 + 42 = \boxed{}$$

Marks

1

7.

$$50 - 40 = \boxed{}$$

1

8.

$$7 + 5 + 9 = \boxed{}$$

Marks

1

9.

$$16 + \boxed{} = 25$$

1

Marks

10.

$$49 - 30 = \boxed{}$$

1

11.

$$10 \times 9 = \boxed{}$$

1

12.

$$30 + 30 = \boxed{}$$

Marks

1

13.

$$2 \times 8 = \boxed{}$$

1

14.

$16 \div 2 =$ [ ]

Marks

1

15.

$50 \div 10 =$ [ ]

1

16.

$$19 - 6 - 4 = \boxed{}$$

Marks

1

17.

$$36 + 47 = \boxed{}$$

1

Marks

18.

$$5 \times 0 = \boxed{}$$

1

19.

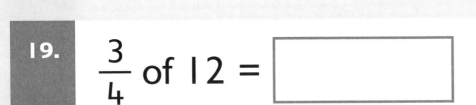

$$\frac{3}{4} \text{ of } 12 = \boxed{}$$

1

20.

$25 + 26 + 10 =$

Marks

1

21.

$54 +$ $= 100$

1

22.

$$35 \div 5 = \boxed{}$$

1

23.

$$\frac{1}{3} \text{ of } 30 = \boxed{}$$

1

24.

$$\boxed{} - 45 = 18$$

Marks

1

25.

$$\frac{1}{2} \text{ of } 54 = \boxed{}$$

1

Test B: Paper 1 Marks

Q	Question	Possible marks	Actual marks
1	3 + 8	1	
2	17 − 10	1	
3	58 + 9	1	
4	4 + 8 + 3	1	
5	35 − 11	1	
6	10 + 42	1	
7	50 − 40	1	
8	7 + 5 + 9	1	
9	16 + ☐ = 25	1	
10	49 − 30	1	
11	10 × 9	1	
12	30 + 30	1	
13	2 × 8	1	
14	16 ÷ 2	1	
15	50 ÷ 10	1	
16	19 − 6 − 4	1	
17	36 + 47	1	
18	5 × 0	1	
19	$\frac{3}{4}$ of 12	1	
20	25 + 26 + 10	1	
21	54 + ☐ = 100	1	
22	35 ÷ 5	1	
23	$\frac{1}{3}$ of 30	1	
24	☐ − 45 = 18	1	
25	$\frac{1}{2}$ of 54	1	
	Total	**25**	

Mathematics

Test B: Paper 2

Instructions Test B: Paper 2

- You have around **35 minutes** for this test paper.

- You may **not use** a calculator to answer any questions in this test paper.

- Work as quickly and carefully as you can.

- Try to answer all the questions. If you cannot do one of the questions, **go on to the next one**. You can come back to it later, if you have time.

- If you finish before the end, **go back and check your work**.

- Ask your teacher if you are not sure what to do.

Follow the instructions for each question carefully.

If you need to do working out, you can use any space on the page – do not use rough paper.

Show your working

You may get extra marks if you show your method when you see this box.

> Show your method.

Aural questions

Any questions which have this icon will be read aloud to you. (The script is on page 94.)

■SCHOLASTIC National Curriculum SATs Tests

Mathematics

Test B: Paper 2

Tom

Beth

Tony

Mrs Green

Marks

Practice question

1.

1

2.

$6 \times 2 = 12$ □

$30 \div 10 = 20$ □

$9 \times 5 = 55$ □

1

3.

Marks

$\dfrac{1}{3}$

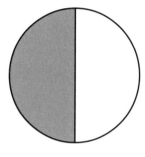

$\dfrac{2}{4}$

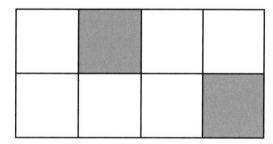

$\dfrac{3}{4}$

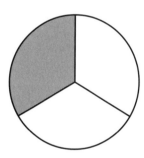

$\dfrac{1}{4}$

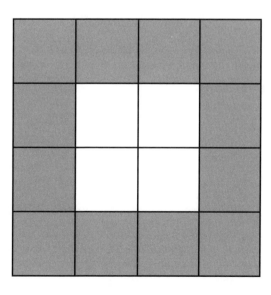

1

4.

Marks

6 o'clock

20 past 9

quarter to 4

five to 6

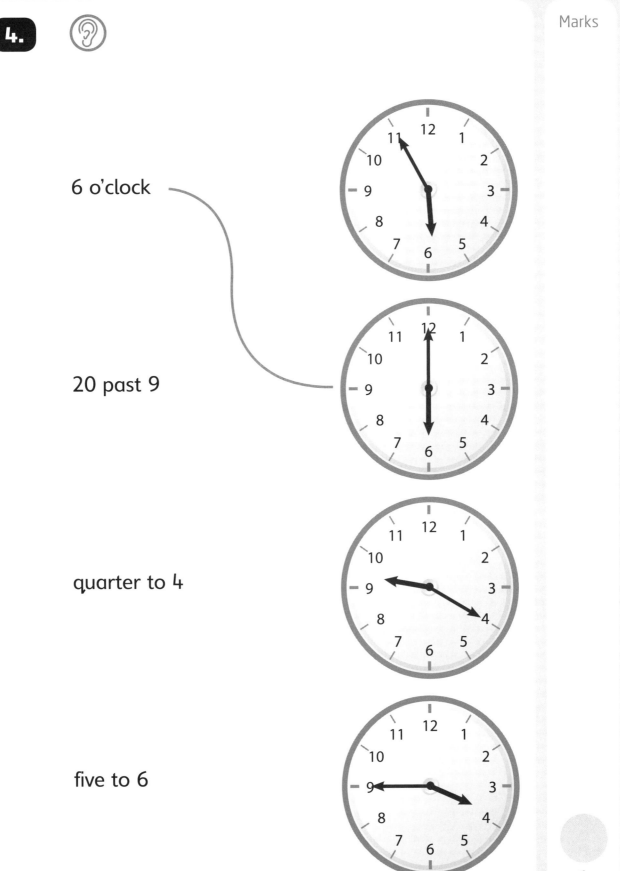

1

5.

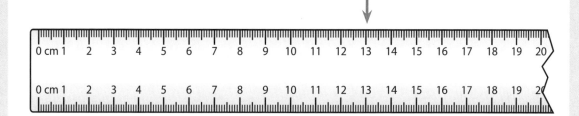

cm

1

6.   42 + 31 = 40 + 2 + 30 + 1

Now complete this in the same way.

25 + 36 = ☐ + ☐ + ☐ + ☐

---

7.   23 + 45 = 68

Now write the answer to this.

68 − 45 = ☐

1

8.

$50 - \boxed{} = 20$

Marks

1

---

9. Write the answers to these number sentences.

$24 - 6 = \boxed{}$

$56 + 20 = \boxed{}$

$6 + 5 + 7 = \boxed{}$

2

10. Look at the time on this clock.

Marks

How many right angles has the minute hand moved through to get to this time?

1

SCHOLASTIC National Curriculum SATs Tests

11. Draw lines to match the correct shape names to the shaded faces.

Marks

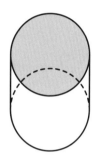

rectangle

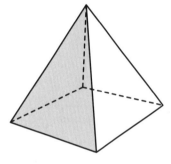

circle

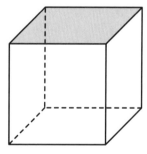

triangle

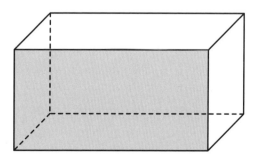

square

1

12. Write these lengths in order. Start with the shortest.

20cm   80cm   30cm

_____   _____   _____

Write **<** or **>** between the lengths.

30cm [   ] 20cm

Marks

1

Marks

13. Write these words as numerals.

fifty-three   thirty-seven

1

Look at these numbers.

37   **93**

Write the correct number in each box.

84 <

47 >

1

14. Read these number sentences.

Put a ✓ by those that are correct.
Put a ✗ by those that are incorrect.

$5 ÷ 35 = 7$ ☐

$6 × 10 = 10 × 6$ ☐

$25 − 4 = 4 − 25$ ☐

$53 + 30 = 30 + 53$ ☐

15. This graph shows which pets children like most.

Marks

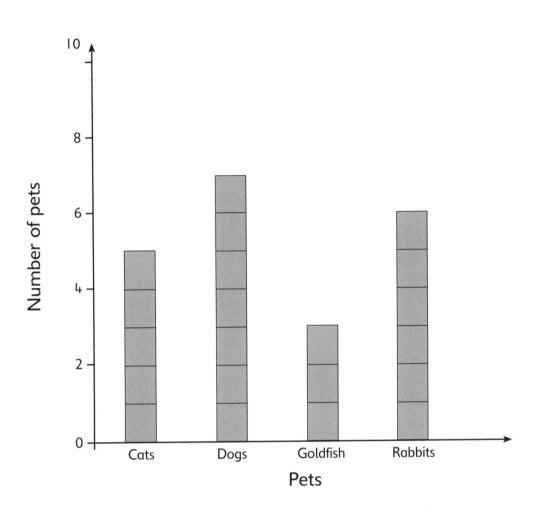

a. How many children like goldfish best?

1

b. How many **more** children chose dogs than cats?

1

16. Write the missing numbers in this number pattern.

Marks

2, 12, 22, _____, _____, _____, _____

Beth wrote some of the numbers in the count of 2.

Write the missing numbers.

40, 38, 36, _____, _____, _____

1

Marks

17. Complete the money addition sentence.

60p +  = £1

1

18. Tom has 35 marbles.

He shares his marbles between 5 pots.

Then he gives 3 of the pots away.

How many marbles does he have left?

 Show your method.

2

Marks

19. Look at these 18 stars.

Circle $\frac{1}{3}$ of the stars.

Complete the fraction number sentence.

$\frac{1}{3}$ of 18 = [   ]

1

SCHOLASTIC National Curriculum SATs Tests

20. Beth says that 45 divided by 5 is the same as 5 divided by 45.

Tony says 45 divided by 5 is not the same as 5 divided by 45.

Who is correct?

Marks

1

---

21. Mrs Green buys some rice for 49p, some carrots for 26p and some onions for 17p. How much change does she get from £1?

 Show your method.

p

2

22. Here is a hundred square.

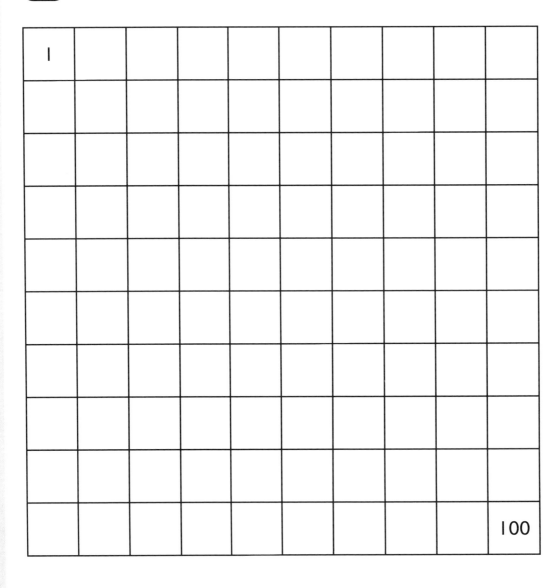

Write these numbers on the square.

43   81   15   72   36

2

23. Class 2W had **25** black pencils on Monday morning.

On Wednesday Class 2W had **36** red pencils.

On Thursday, there were **43** red and black pencils altogether.

How many pencils had been lost?

 Show your method.

Marks

2

24. Draw in one line of symmetry on each shape.

2

25. The shopkeeper has 5 packs of 10 black pencils.

She sells 3 pencils.

How many pencils does she have left?

Marks

 Show your method.

2

Test B: Paper 2 Marks

Q	Strand	Sub-strand	Possible marks	Actual marks
1	Addition and subtraction	Add/subtract mentally	1	
2	Multiplication and division	Calculate mathematical statements for multiplication and division within the multiplication tables	1	
3	Fractions, decimals, percentages	Recognise, find, name and write fractions; equivalent fractions	1	
4	Measurement	Telling time	1	
5	Measurement	Estimate, measure and read scales	1	
6	Number and place value	Place value	1	
7	Addition and subtraction	Estimate, use inverses and check	1	
8	Number and place value	Number problems	1	
9	Addition and subtraction	Add/subtract mentally	2	
10	Geometry – position and movement	Describe position, direction and movement (right angles)	1	
11	Geometry – properties of shapes	Identify 2D shapes on the surface of 3D shapes	1	
12	Measurement	Compare, describe and order measures	1	
13	Number and place value	Read, write and compare numbers	2	
14	Addition, subtraction, multiplication and division	Order of numbers in calculations	2	
15	Statistics	Solve problems involving data	2	
16	Number and place value	Counting in steps	1	
17	Measurement	Money	1	
18	Multiplication and division	Solve problems involving multiplication and division	2	
19	Fractions	Recognise, find, name and write fractions	1	
20	Multiplication and division	Order of numbers in division	1	
21	Measurement	Solve problems involving money	2	
22	Number and place value	Identify, represent, and estimate; rounding	2	
23	Addition and subtraction	Add/subtract to solve problems	2	
24	Geometry – properties of shapes	Describe properties and classify shapes (symmetry)	2	
25	Multiplication and division	Solve problems involving multiplication and division	2	
		Total	**35**	

Marks & guidance

Marking and assessing the papers

The mark schemes provide details of correct answers including guidance for questions that have more than one mark.

Interpreting answers

Problem	Guidance
Digit has been written in reverse.	A reversed digit is acceptable if it is clearly recognisable as the digit intended. For example, a reversed 2 must clearly show the characteristics of a 2 rather than a 5.
The number has been transposed in the answer.	Transposed numbers should not be awarded the mark. For example, an answer of '16' when the correct answer is '61' should not be marked as correct.
The answer is equivalent to the one in the mark scheme.	The mark scheme will generally specify which equivalent responses are allowed. If this is not the case, award the mark unless the mark scheme states otherwise. For example: $1\frac{1}{2}$ or 1.5
The answer is correct but the wrong working is shown.	Always award the mark(s) for a correct response unless the mark scheme states otherwise.
The correct response has been crossed (or rubbed) out and not replaced.	Do not award the mark(s) for legible crossed-out answers that have not been replaced or that have been replaced by a further incorrect attempt.
The answer has been worked out correctly but an incorrect answer has been written in the answer box.	Give precedence to the answer given in the answer box over any other workings. There may be cases where the incorrect answer is due to a transcription error. You may check the child's intention and decide whether to award the mark.
More than one answer is given.	If all answers given are correct (or a range of answers is given, all of which are correct), award the mark unless the mark scheme states otherwise. If both correct and incorrect responses are given, do not award the mark unless the mark scheme states otherwise.

Problem	Guidance
There appears to be a misread of numbers affecting the working.	In general, the mark should not be awarded. However, in two-mark questions that have a working mark, award one mark if the working is applied correctly using the misread numbers, provided that the misread numbers are comparable in difficulty to the original numbers. For example, if '243' is misread as '234', both numbers may be regarded as comparable in difficulty.
No answer is given in the expected place, but the correct answer is given elsewhere.	Where a child has shown understanding of the question, award the mark. In particular, where a word or number response is expected, a child may meet the requirement by annotating a graph or labelling a diagram elsewhere in the question.

Written methods for addition and subtraction

The following guidance shows some written methods suitable for Key Stage 1.

Addition

25 + 34   = 20 + 5 + 30 + 4

              = 20 + 30 + 5 + 4

              = 50 + 9

              = 59

```
    2  5  =  2  0  +  5
 +  3  4  =  3  0  +  4
 ─────────────────────────
    5  9     5  0  +  9
```

Subtraction

54 − 33

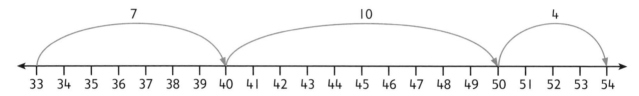

54 − 33 = 7 + 10 + 4 = 21

```
    5  4  =  5  0  +  4
 −  3  3  =  3  0  +  3
 ─────────────────────────
    2  1     2  0  +  1
```

National standard in maths

The mark that each child gets in the test paper will be known as the 'raw score' (for example, '37' in 37/60). The raw score will be converted to a scaled score and children achieving a scaled score of 100 or more will achieve the national standard in that subject. These 'scaled scores' enable results to be reported consistently year-on-year.

The guidance in the table below shows the marks that children need to achieve to reach the national standard. This should be treated as a guide only, as the number of marks may vary. You can also find up-to-date information about scaled scores on our website: www.scholastic.co.uk/nationaltests

Marks achieved	Standard
0–35	Has not met the national standard in mathematics for KS1
36–60	Has met the national standard in mathematics for KS1

Aural questions

Explain to the children that you will read aloud some questions for them to answer. Tell them that you will read each question twice only, leaving a short gap in-between. Tell the children that they must listen very carefully when you read the questions.

Do the practice question together. Check that the children have written the answer in the box.

Read aloud questions 1 to 5 and repeat the question (the bold text only). Tell the children that they must work on their own and they must not call out the answers.

Remember to repeat the question. Repeat the bold text only. At the end of each question, allow sufficient time for the children to complete what they can.

TEST A, PAPER 2 (pages 28–32)

Practice question: **What is 5 add 4?** Write your answer in the box.

1. **What is 19 add 6?** Write your answer in the box.
2. **Join the shapes to their names.**
3. **Look at the thermometer. What temperature is shown?** Write your answer in the box.
4. **This tally chart shows the fruit the children like to eat. How many children like oranges?** Write your answer in the box.
5. **Circle one third of the buttons below.** Write your answer in the box.

TEST B, PAPER 2 (pages 68–71)

Practice question: **What is 65 subtract 20?** Write your answer in the box.

1. **What is the total of three, four, and seven?** Write your answer in the box.
2. **Mark Jamie's homework. Put a tick if the answer is correct. Put a cross if the answer is incorrect.** Write your answer in the boxes.
3. **Here are some fractions. Join these to the correct shaded shape.**
4. **Draw lines to match the times to the clocks. One has been done to help you.**
5. **Look at the ruler. What length is shown by the arrow?** Write your answer in the box.

Q	Answers	Marks
Practice	9	
1	13	1
2	7	1
3	20	1
4	47	1
5	19	1
6	41	1
7	1	1
8	4	1
9	33	1
10	42	1
11	0	1
12	29	1
13	20	1
14	60	1
15	20	1
16	5	1
17	92	1
18	25	1
19	6	1
20	38	1
21	22	1
22	4	1
23	95	1
24	28	1
25	10	1
	Total	**25**

Q	Answers	Marks
Practice	9	
1	25	1
2	Award 1 mark only if all answers are correct.	1
3	28°C	1
4	12	1
5	6 Award 1 mark if 6 buttons are circled or marked in some way.	1
6	61 < 63 54 > 45 Award 1 mark only if both answers are correct.	1
7	✓ ✗ Award 1 mark only if both answers are correct.	1
8	Circled digits are: 3, 2, 9 Circled digits are: 4, 3, 6 Award 1 mark only if all answers are correct.	1
9	◯	1
10	7p	1

Q	Answers	Marks
11	÷	1
12	Macco	1
13	86p	1
14	**a.** Check that 57 has been written in the box.	1
	b. Check that the position of 52 has been estimated correctly.	1
15	30p Award 2 marks for the correct answer of 30p. If the answer is incorrect, award 1 mark for evidence of appropriate working, for example: 15 + 20 = 35 35 × 2 = 70 £1 − 70p = incorrect answer	2
16	**a.** 1kg, $1\frac{1}{2}$kg, 2kg	1
	b. 2kg > 1kg 1kg < $1\frac{1}{2}$kg	1
17	65 Award 2 marks for the correct answer. If the answer is incorrect, award 1 mark for evidence of appropriate working, for example: 63 − 17 = 46 46 + 19 = incorrect answer	2
18	**a.** 9, 12, 15, 18	1
	b. 48, 45, 42, 39, 36	1

19

Shape	Number of edges	Number of vertices	Number of faces
	2	0	3
	1	0	2
	9	6	5
	8	5	5

2

Award 2 marks only if all information is correct.

Award 1 mark if half or more of the data is correct.

20 94

1

21

Award 1 mark only if all answers are correct.

Do not award the mark if more than one time is matched to one clock.

1

22 **a.** Check that 12 chocolate squares have been circled.

1

b. $\frac{2}{4} = \frac{1}{2}$

1

Q	Answers	Marks
23	18 Award 2 marks for the correct answer. If the answer is incorrect, award 1 mark for evidence of appropriate working, for example: $20 \div 2 = 10$ $16 \div 2 = 8$ $10 + 8 =$ incorrect answer	2
24	**a.** 6 **b.** 3	1 1
25	 **a.** Award mark if route has been drawn correctly. **b.** Award mark if route has been drawn correctly.	2
	Total	35

Q	Answers	Marks
Practice	2	
1	11	1
2	7	1
3	67	1
4	15	1
5	24	1
6	52	1
7	10	1
8	21	1
9	9	1
10	19	1
11	90	1
12	60	1
13	16	1
14	8	1
15	5	1
16	9	1
17	83	1
18	0	1
19	9	1
20	61	1
21	46	1
22	7	1
23	10	1
24	63	1
25	27	1
	Total	**25**

SCHOLASTIC National Curriculum SATs Tests

Mark scheme Test B: Paper 2 (pages 66–88)

Q	Answers	Marks
Practice	45	
1	14	1
2	✓ ✗ ✗ Award 1 mark only if all answers are correct.	1
3	Award 1 mark only if all answers are correct.	1
4	Award 1 mark only if all answers are correct.	1
5	13cm	1
6	20 + 5 + 30 + 6	1
7	23	1
8	30	1
9	18 76 18 Award 2 marks if all answers are correct. Award 1 mark if two are correct.	2

Q	Answers	Marks
10	2	1
11	rectangle, circle, triangle, square connected to 3D shapes Award 1 mark only if all answers are correct.	1
12	20cm, 30cm, 80cm > Award 1 mark only if both answers are correct. Answers to the first part need to show cm for each length.	1
13	**a.** 53, 37 **b.** 84 < 93 47 > 37 Award 1 mark only if both answers are correct.	1 1
14	✗ ✓ ✗ ✓ Award 2 marks only if all answers are correct. If three answers are correct, award 1 mark.	2
15	**a.** 3 **b.** 2	1 1
16	32, 42, 52, 62 34, 32, 30 Award 1 mark only if all answers are correct.	1
17	40p	1
18	14 Award 2 marks for the correct answer. If the answer is incorrect, award 1 mark for evidence of appropriate working, for example: 35 ÷ 5 = 7 7 × 2 = incorrect	2

SCHOLASTIC National Curriculum SATs Tests

Q	Answers	Marks
19	6 Award 1 mark for the correct answer.	1
20	Tony	1
21	8p Award 2 marks for the correct answer. If the answer is incorrect, award 1 mark for evidence of appropriate working, for example: 49 + 26 + 17 = 40 + 20 + 10 + 9 + 6 + 7 = 70 + 15 + 7 = 85 + 7 = 92 100 − 92 = incorrect answer	2

22

1									
			15						
					36				
			43						
		72							
81									
									100

Award 2 marks for all correct.

Award 1 mark for 3 or 4 correct.

Marks: 2

Q	Answers	Marks
23	18 Award 2 marks for the correct answer. If the answer is incorrect, award 1 mark for evidence of appropriate working, for example: 25 + 36 = 20 + 30 + 5 + 6 = 50 + 11 = 61 61 − 43 = incorrect answer	2
24	Check that each shape has a correct line of symmetry drawn in. Award 2 marks only if all shapes are completed correctly. Award 1 mark if 6 or 7 shapes are completed correctly.	2
25	47 Award 2 marks for the correct answer. If the answer is incorrect, award 1 mark for evidence of appropriate working, for example: 10 × 5 = 50 50 − 3 = incorrect answer	2
	Total	**35**